" Yet slowly, surely, steadily, in the course of my fifteen visits, the proportions adjusted themselves to the facts, and I came at last to realize that a waterfall a hundred and sixty-five feet high and a quarter of a mile wide was an impressive thing. It was not a dipperful to my vanished great vision, but it would answer. "

- MARK TWAIN

MARK TWAIN'S

Niagara

the graphic novel

A!H COMICS

PUBLISHED BY
Alternate History Comics Inc.

STORY & CREATIVE CONSULTANT
Zachary Schwartz

COVER ART
Shane Kirshenblatt

BOOK 1 | ISBN
978-0-9877152-7-2

FIRST PRINTING
Printed in Canada

#

I grew up in St. Catharines, a city adjacent to Niagara Falls in Southern Ontario, where my family and I visited often enough to call the Niagara Region "home".

A childhood friend of mine, Zachary Schwartz, was always a passionate, creative and forward-thinking fellow. This was the kid you always wanted to play with. He had the innate ability to make every toy, board game or physical activity not just entertainment – but also an adventure.

When life took us away from each other to opposite ends of the continent, I wondered if we would ever have a chance to go on another adventure. Then, ten years ago, but twenty years later, Zachary – after racking up an impressive resume in film and stage production in L.A. and New York, including roles in 28 films before the age of 21 - came to me with an incredible story. This original story was *Mark Twain's Niagara*.

Mark Twain (Samuel Clemens), best known for *The Adventures of Huckleberry Finn*, wrote passionately about the Niagara Region after his first visit by steam train in the 1860's. In 1893, he published his own short story, "Niagara" in the collection *Sketches, Old and New*. Zachary first read this story when he was younger and was immediately captivated. As an adult, he could not fathom how contemporary Twain literature fans, as well as Niagara Falls enthusiasts, had not heard of this story before - written by one of the most famous authors of our time. With this, Zachary spent years crafting a feature length screenplay based on Twain's own experiences in the region, set to the backdrop of the thundering Niagara Falls.

The original screenplay is not just an adaptation of Twain's "Niagara" short story - it also features events and accounts recorded by Twain later in life. Told from the perspective of an old man, this story follows a version of Twain in his 30's as he crosses borders by steam train into Niagara for the first time in his lifetime.

This graphic novel features a roster of award-winning and legendary artists and authors, including: Ty Templeton, Claude St. Aubin, Micah Farritor, Shane Kirshenblatt, Mike Rooth, Ben Shannon,

Richard Pace, David Cutler, Menton J. Matthews III, Nicholas Burns, Haiwei Hou, Keith Grachow, Jake Allen and Frank Reynoso.

You'll notice that Chapter 6 in this book, 'Ghosts', has a slightly different tone than the rest of the story. This chapter was written by Fred Kennedy, radio personality and comic book author (*Teuton*, *The Fourth Planet*, *True Patriot*). Fred is a detailed author and an avid history buff. It was enthralling to have him write a chapter of this story, and help shape the second act.

I encourage you to read the Biographies section at the back of this book to learn more about the creators involved. Every artist and author pulled out the stops to make this story come to life.

This book is in fact one single story, told over several chapters, with each chapter being illustrated by a different one of our incredible artists. In this way, the past comes to life in a way you've never quite seen before.

That was one of the goals of creating the *Mark Twain's Niagara* graphic novel - to take the reader on an unexpected adventure of a lifetime, through legend and history.

This is just the type of story that AH Comics was created to publish - stories that pull in the reader, entertains, and empowers us to question the incredible. How do we know if the events illustrated here did or did not happen? Are the most incredible parts of the story the made up ones, or are they real, hidden among the backdrop of the thundering Falls?

For the most part, I believe readers want a dash of familiar with a splash of the unknown. The cover art was created with this in mind. The concept behind this wonderful hand-painted piece by artist Shane Kirshenblatt is to give the viewer a sense of intrigue, nostalgia, excitement and wonder.

From cover to cover, the aim is to keep the spirit of adventure alive – for graphic novel readers, for Mark Twain fans, for the Niagara Region, its history, and for the spirits of two childhood friends who have probably never grown up.

On behalf of Zachary and myself, this is for our parents.

– Andy Stanleigh
President AH Comics

Chapters

Chapter 1
The Beginning

Did you know?

The mansion in Elmira, New York that most people picture as Twain's own home, was in fact the home of his in-laws, the Langdons. Most of the author's works were written in a small building separate from the Elmira mansion; a short walk to Quarry Farm. There, in a small cottage built to resemble the pilot house of a riverboat overlooking the Chemung River Valley, Samuel Clemens created stories.

BANG!

MAN HAS MADE A THOUSAND LUXURIES AND CALLED THEM NECESSITIES, AND SATISFIED NOTHING.

QUIT YOUR WHINING AND LEND ME A HAND.

JAMES, I AM AT YOUR SERVICE.

BUT MY SERVICES ARE FAR BETTER SERVED AFTER *LUNCH*.

THAT WAS DELICIOUS.

YOU KNOW I BROUGHT US SOMETHING *SPECIAL* FOR DESSERT.

CHOCOLATE FROM HERSHEY, PENNSYLVANIA?

A FRIEND BROUGHT THIS FROM RUSSIA.

THAT'S THE SEAL OF THE CZAR!

ITS NICHOLAS' *PERSONAL* BRAND, NO ONE ELSE BUT HIM...

...AND US.

AND US.

NOW THEN, WITHOUT DELAY...

NOW NOW, YOU BROUGHT YOUR BEST, SO I'LL BRING *MINE*.

LET'S GO TO MY STUDY.

HM.... WHERE *IS* IT....

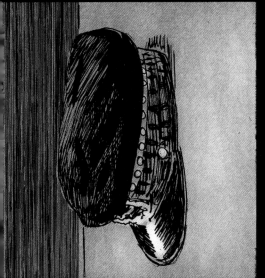

The Prince and the Pauper | The Prince and the Pauper | Huckleberry Finn | Huckleberry Finn | Huckleberry Finn | Tom Sawyer | Tom Sawyer | Tom Sawyer | Tom Sawyer

EUREKA!

CAREFUL NOW, SAMUEL.

I'M AN OLD MAN.

I FOUND IT!

Chapter 2
The Arrival

Did you know?

If it was not for the development of the steam rail system, Niagara Falls would not be the destination it is today. With the arrival of trains, came the arrival of many cultures and peoples into Niagara to help develop the region's power and thriving tourist industry.

"THE GUIDE MOVED FROM HISTORY TO STORY. HE RECOUNTED HOW HE SAW A MIGHTY LITTLE STEAM BOAT NAVIGATE AND DESCEND THE FEARFUL RAPIDS BELOW..."

"...THE PADDLE BOX DIPPED BELOW THE RAGING BILLOWS. HER SMOKE STACK TOPPLED OVER BOARD AND HER PLANKING BEGAN TO PART ASUNDER..."

"...UNTIL THE STEAMBOAT FINALLY COMPLETED HER MISSION DOWN THE DEVILS HOLE."

"THE MAID OF THE MIST SURVIVED THE GREAT NIAGARA RIVER."

"IT WAS WORTH THE PRICE OF ADMISSION JUST TO HEAR THE GUIDE TELL THE STORY NINE TIMES IN SUCCESSION TO DIFFERENT PARTIES. HE NEVER MISSES A WORD OR ALTERS A SENTENCE OR GESTURE."

"AFTER A FASHION I WAS QUITE WET ENOUGH, AND DECIDED TO MOVE ON".

Chapter 3
The Magnificent

Did you know?

Many immigrants came to the Niagara Region for work, including international artists, and daredevils. Jean Francois Gravelet - the "Great Blondin" came into Niagara from France. From Italy came Maria Spelterina, who was the only woman to cross the Niagara River Gorge on tightrope.

DUNKIRK THE MAGNIFICENT!

NOW WATCH AS I STROLL ABOUT THE CATARACT AS THOUGH IT WERE MY VERY PLAYGROUND!

GASP AS I STARE DEATH *IN THE FACE!*

Chapter 4

A Grape Voyage

Did you know?

One of the earliest known recordings of the practice
of "pigeage" - grape stomping - can be seen carved
onto a sarcophagus from the 3rd century AD, Rome.
Today, the Grape & Wine Festival in Niagara has
been celebrated for three quarters of a century,
and includes many local wineries participating in
celebratory grape stomping events.

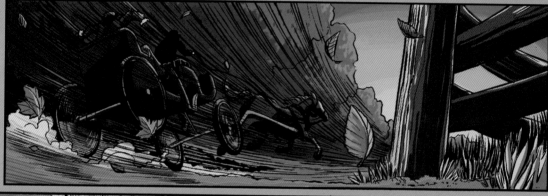

Chapter 5

The War

Did you know?

Today, at the top of the hill on Lundy's Lane is one of the most popular tourist destinations in Niagara with shops, attractions and restaurants. But over two hundred years ago, this was the scene of the Battle of Lundy's Lane during the War of 1812. It became known as one of the deadliest battles ever fought in Canada.

Chapter 6
Ghosts

Did you know?

The Olde Angel Inn is home to one of the most famous hauntings of the Niagara Region - the British Captain Swayze. Captain Swayze was an officer who is said to have been killed in the Inn's wine cellar by his own troops. Still operating after 150 years, it is said his ghost haunts the Inn to this very day.

Chapter 7
The Hotel

Did you know?

The original Clifton Hotel first opened in the 1830's, only to be burned down twice. In 1898 the hotel was entirely destroyed by fire. After being rebuilt and reopening in 1905, it burned down again, this time on New Year's Eve, 1932. Today, only photographs remain of the original hotel.

"I HAD READ OF THE CLIFTON HOUSE BEFORE MY ARRIVAL."

"A COLLEAGUE OF MINE STAYED THERE, AS WELL AS SEVERAL PROMINENT AMERICAN POLITICIANS."

"IT WAS A WORLD-FAMOUS DESTINATION FOR EUROPEAN ROYALTY AND CELEBRITIES ALIKE."

WELCOME TO THE CLIFTON HOUSE, SIR!

"IT WAS A SONG I LEARNED ON THE OL' MISS, WHEN I RAN MY OWN BOAT."

"IT COMES IN HANDY TO HAVE A SONG IN YOUR HEART."

OSCAR WILDE STAYED AT THE CLIFTON HOUSE...

WHAT?

...QUEEN VICTORIA'S NEPHEW STAYED THERE TOO.

AND THE UNDERGROUND RAILROAD RAN RIGHT THROUGH THE GREAT LAKE BASIN NEAR THE HOUSE, YES?

I KNOW. I KNEW THAT! I WAS TELLING THE STORY!

YOU SORTA STOPPED FOR A LONG TIME THERE.

Chapter 8
Underground

Did you know?

The Niagara River and Gorge was one of the final crossing points of freedom for enslaved individuals and families following the Underground Railroad. After reaching their final destination, many of those individuals found themselves staying, or eventually returning to Niagara Falls to help contribute to the economic and social growth of the area.

Chapter 9
The Stranger

Did you know?

In a letter to Samuel Moffett, written in 1904, Mark Twain wrote, "*None but the Deity can tell what is good luck and what is bad before the returns are all in.*" Gambling was a contributing factor to the tourist atmosphere in Niagara Falls through history. Before the city officially supported public casinos, popular private houses and shady individuals alike offered games of chance for willing participants.

HOWDY, STRANGER.

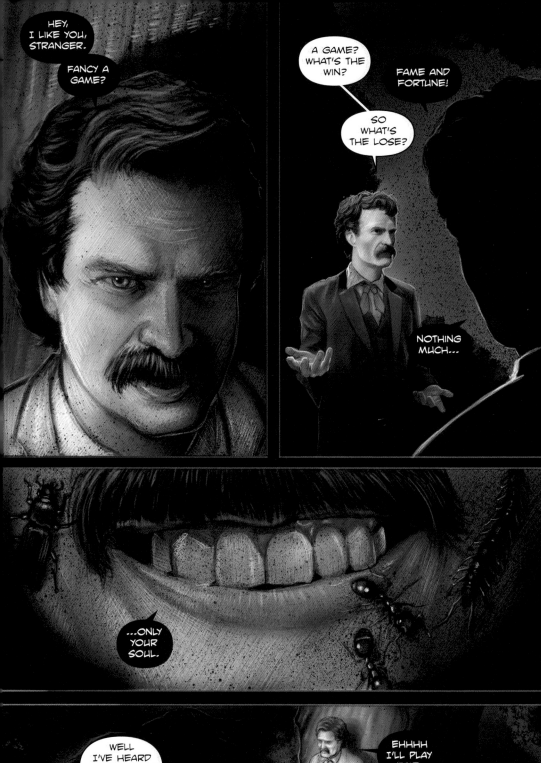

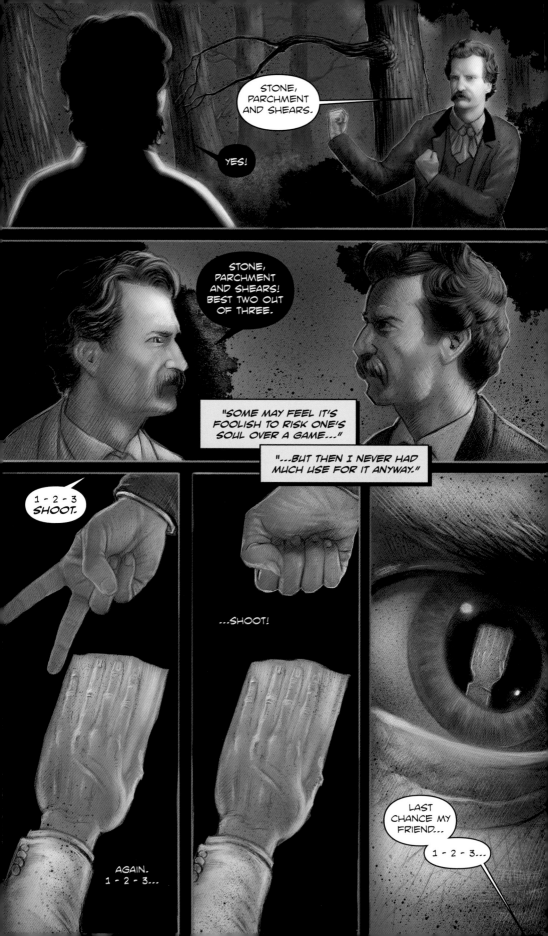

Chapter 10

Into the Unknown

Did you know?

At 10:00pm on September 14, 1860, the
Niagara Falls were illuminated at night
for the first time in history.

"AS I PREPARED FOR BED, I THOUGHT OF ALL THE WONDERS OF THAT DAY."

"BEFORE I KNEW IT..."

"...I WAS FAST ASLEEP AND DREAMING OF SUCH WONDROUS THINGS."

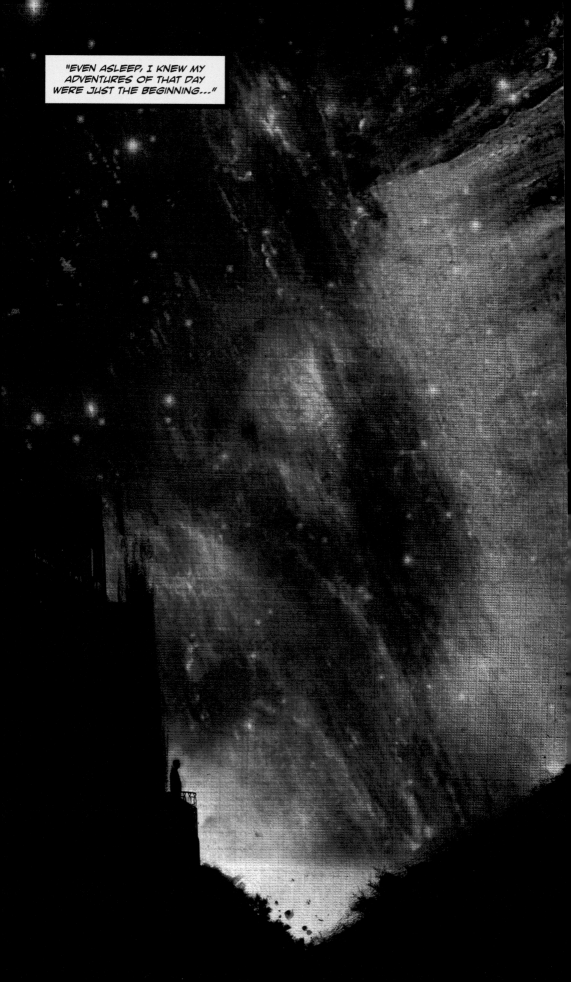

To be continued...

MARK TWAIN
WAS THE FIRST TO

THE FALLS!

OR

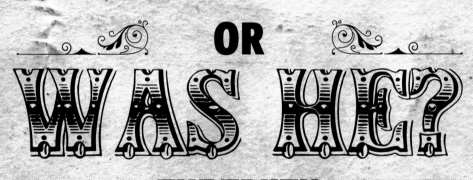

THE TRUTH
IS
COMING

MARK TWAIN
WAS A RENOWNED
MONSTER
FIGHTER!
OR
WAS HE?
THE TRUTH
IS
COMING

Did you know?

MARK TWAIN
WAS THE FIRST

TIME

TRAVELLER!

OR

WAS HE?

THE TRUTH

IS
COMING

Did you know?

MARK TWAIN'S GHOST APPEARS IN

THE MIST

ONCE A YEAR!

OR

DOES IT?

THE TRUTH IS COMING

BEN SHANNON

Ben is a Toronto based graphic artist, illustrator and animator working for print, TV, film and online. His clients include Marvel, DC Comics, National Geographic, Rolling Stone, The Globe & Mail, The National Post, The Wall Street Journal, Nike, Universal Music, Global, Rogers, CBC and more. He was the winner of the 2008 ADCC interactive Design Award and the Applied Arts Award for Illustration Excellence in 1998. As well, Ben's animation was nominated for a Canadian Screen Award in 2014.

CLAUDE ST. AUBIN

Claude is a Joe Shuster Award winning illustrator, and has been inducted into the Canadian Comic Book Hall of Fame. He has worked on many popular titles including *R.E.B.E.L.S.*, *Justice League of America*, *Green Lantern*, *Aquaman*, the cult favourite *Mars Attacks The Savage Dragon*, *Action Comics*, *Green Arrow*, and the *War of 1812* - which won the 2014 Alberta Book of the Year Publishing Award.

DAVID CUTLER

David is a Newfoundland-born artist based in Toronto, Canada. Working in comics for almost a decade, David is a frequent special guest artist at national shows and events. His comic book work has appeared in various publications, magazines and series including: *Wonderland*, *Robyn Hood vs Red Riding Hood*, *Snow White vs Snow White*, *The Secret World of Glacier Thorne*, *Hacktivist*, *Northern Guard* and *Adventure Time*.

FRANK REYNOSO

Frank is an illustrator, colourist and author. His work has appeared in the popular anthology *Occupy Comics*, and in *World War 3 Illustrated*. He has worked with House of 12's *Touching Children's Stories*, Terminal Press's hit series *Zombie Bomb*, the website HiLo Brow, Drawmore Inc.'s *Nobodies Vol. 2* and *Nomads: Tales from the Edge of the World*. His illustrations have appeared in *The Democratic Left*, *Mayfair Games*, and *Physics of the Impossible* for the Science Channel.

HAIWEI HOU

Haiwei is an internationally renowned illustrator, animator, character and conceptual artist. She has worked all over the world, from California to China to Vancouver. Her work can be seen in magazines, television, film, books and games. Haiwei has worked on high profile projects for Nelvana Animation, Nickelodeon, EA Games and Sideshow Collectibles designing figures of Iron Man, the Dark Knight, The Hulk and more. Her animated film, *Vernal Equinox*, has been screened across the globe, winning numerous selections and awards.

FRED KENNEDY

Award-winning national radio and television personality 'Fearless' Fred Kennedy (*102.1 The Edge, Teletoon at Night*) is also a critically successful comic book author, working on the popular titles *Teuton*, *Remnant*, and *The Fourth Planet*. He won the Steve Young Broadcaster of the Year Award in 2009, the same year he co-founded the fan favourite independent publishing house BigSexyComics. He continues to be a frequent special guest creator at comic book shows and events in Toronto.

JAKE ALLEN

Jake is an accomplished comic book artist and illustrator, working on the title *Brownsville* (NBM Publishing) and *Kings & Canvas* (Monkeybrain Comics), both written by Xeric Award winning author Neil Kleid. Jake is also a graduate of the Kubert School of Cartoon and Graphic Art - founded by legendary DC Comics artist and creator Joe Kubert.

JEFFREY VEREGGE

Jeffrey is an award winning artist and illustrator of the Port Gamble S'Klallam Tribe, also with both Suquamish and Duwamish tribal ancestry. His work in mainstream comics can be seen in the titles *G.I. Joe*, *Captain America*, *Judge Dredd*, *New Avengers* and *Red Wolf*. He consciously blends a Native perspective with his visual art, which has led him to being named one of the Top 60 Masters of Contemporary Art of 2013 from ArtTour International, New York, NY, as well as creating one of The Top 100 Comic Book Covers of 2014 as recognized by IGN.

KEITH GRACHOW

Keith Grachow an illustrator for graphic novels and children's books with over two decades of commercial success. He has worked for companies like Play Along Toys (a subsidiary of Jakks Pacific) on the *Bruce Lee, Enter the Dragon series*; and for Disney Animation, as a digital ink and paint artist on the animated flicks *Princess and the Frog* and the reboot of *Winnie the Pooh* (2011). He has self published a series of action adventure children's books with his mom Amy Grachow, called *Up-In-The-Sky*. He is also the co-founder of Kika Mika Comics, who have released *Concrete Martians*, *Polybius Dreams*, and the Joe Shuster Gene Day Award nominated series *Saltwater*.

MARK TWAIN

Mark Twain was the pen name of the celebrated author Samuel L. Clemens. Of his many works, Twain wrote two classics of American literature: *The Adventures of Tom Sawyer* and *The Adventures of Huckleberry Finn*. He was also a riverboat pilot, travel journalist, lecturer and inventor.

MICAH FARRITOR

Micah is an artist, colourist and traditional media illustrator who has worked with READ Magazine, IDW and more. He has created work for popular titles such as *Sleepy Hollow*, *Spoon River*, *War of the Worlds*, *White Picket Fences*, *Strange Girl* and *The Wind Raider*. Micah was also a contributing artist for *Science Fiction Classics* and the pre-war narrative collection *Postcards: True Stories That Never Happened*.

MENTON J MATTHEWS III

As an award-winning American painter, illustrator, and comic book artist currently living in Chicago, menton3 (Menton J. Matthews III) has created work for Image Comics and IDW, most notably on the hugely successful *MONOCYTE* series, as well as *Memory Collectors*, *X-Files*, *Zombies vs. Robots*, *Crawl to Me*, *Silent Hill* and *Three Feathers*. His fine art paintings have been shown in prominent galleries including La Luz De Jesus, Strychnin Gallery, COPRO Gallery and Last Rites Gallery.

MIKE ROOTH

Fan-favourite Mike Rooth Hails from Oakville, Ontario, and holds over a decade of commercial success as an illustrator, working on numerous educational graphic novels, as well as Marvel and DC Comics sketch card sets. He is a popular cover artist working on titles like *Red Sonja*, *Captain Cannuck*, *Animosity*, *Ray Fawkes' Intersect*, *Backways*, *Quantum & Woody*, *Shadowman*, *Pathfinder*, and the popular graphic novel *WidowsWake*, which he co-created with his wife, Erika.

NICHOLAS BURNS

Nicholas is an author, storyboard artist, award-winning fine artist and film-maker. In the 1980's, while in Rankin Inlet, NWT (now Nunavut) he wrote and drew *Arctic Comics*, *Super Shamou*, *True North*, and several other educational comics for federal and territorial agencies. He also helped form, and chaired, the community's first library board. In the 1990's he contributed comic art to *Sunburn*, has written for Kitchen Sink, Metal Hurlant, DC Comics, and storyboarded a long list of feature films including *Curse of Chucky* and *The Lookout*.

RICHARD PACE

Richard is a multiple award-winning illustrator and author. In his early career, his art and design work drew acclaim working with Tree House Press, creating award-winning educational and poetry books for children and schools. With over 20 years in the industry, he is now an author, illustrator and cover artist for many popular titles in the market today, including Batman, Doctor Strange, X-Men, Captain Marvel, Pitt and more.

SHANE KIRSHENBLATT

Shane Kirshenblatt is a Canadian writer, artist, painter and sculptor. He is known for Dorothy Gale: Journey to Oz , Grave Conditions, the massive Jewish Comix Anthology and the popular Toronto Comix Anthology. Shane is also an art teacher, regularly running comic-themed workshops through the Ontario Art Council's Artist In The Classroom program in the Greater Toronto Area.

TY TEMPLETON

The legendary Ty Templeton is a Canadian Comic Book Hall of Fame artist, and has won several Eisner Awards for both his illustration and writing. His comic book work includes some of the biggest titles in the industry: *Batman*, *Superman*, *Spider-man*, *The Avengers*, *The Simpsons* and more. Ty is also an acclaimed mentor and teacher, supporting new talent in the industry with his series of "Comic Book Boot Camp" classes in Toronto, Canada.

ZACHARY SCHWARTZ

Zach has an extremely long resume as an actor in film, television and stage productions, including roles in 28 films before the age of 21. His work in film includes cult favourites such as *Bride of Chucky* and *Boondock Saints*. His television appearances include *Midsummer Night's Dream*, *Clear Water* and *Kids in the Hall*. On stage, Zach has performed in *Sweeney Todd*, *Rocky Horror Picture Show*, *Crazy For You*, *Oliver*, *Jesus Christ Superstar*, *Little Shop of Horrors* and *Grease*. He has completed elite programs and certificates from the American Music and Dramatic Academy, New York, the Meisner Certificate in Dramatic Arts from JoAnne Barron D. W. Brown Studio in Los Angeles, California and Improvisation Consummate at Second City, Toronto.

"Sail away from the safe harbor. Catch the trade winds in your sails. Explore. Dream." — MARK TWAIN

About AH Comics

Alternate History Comics Inc (AH Comics) publishes award-winning, original comic book and graphic novels focusing on history, fantasy, art and culture.

Our books include the 2011 critically successful debut publication *Titan: An Alternate History*, the Juno Award Nominee shortlisted title *The River Pilots' Delta*, the massive *Jewish Comix Anthology Volumes 1 & 2*, the award-nominated graphic novel series *Hobson's Gate* (nominated for an Association of Arts and Social Change Canadian Publishing Award, and an AASC People's Choice Award) and the multiple-award winning *MOONSHOT The Indigenous Comics Collection Volumes 1 & 2*.

Volume 1 of our *MOONSHOT* collection was named "The Best Book of 2015" by the School Library Journal (the largest book reviewer in the world). Both *MOONSHOT* Volume 1 & 2 were awarded Bronze Medals for "Best Graphic Novel - Drama/Documentary" at the Independent Publisher's Awards in 2016 and 2018 respectively. At the time of this printing, Volume 2 of the *MOONSHOT* collection has also been nominated for a First Nations Community READ award.

We are proud to have created a library of original graphic novels and collections that have involved over 100 authors and artists from across the globe, connecting people with their stories, histories and fans. AH Comics always strives to be inclusive, accurate and positive in the representation of characters and their creators.

We regularly give back to the community by donating hundreds of books to schools and libraries in Canada and the US, as well as a portion of proceeds to mental health charities in Canada.

For more information or to contact AH Comics visit:
www.ahcomics.com.

> " *A successful book is not made of what is in it, but of what is left out of it.* "

MARK TWAIN
Letter to Henry H. Rogers, pp26–pp28, April 1897.